The cat saw a mouse.

1

She wanted the mouse...

but the mouse ran away.

The dog saw the cat…

but the cat ran away.

A man saw the mouse...

and the cat… and the dog.

He ran and ran.

He stopped the dog.

He stopped the cat.

He wanted the mouse...

but the mouse got away.